Preface

Efforts made in recent years to provide a wider choice of reading material for children have been warmly welcomed by teachers. Experience has shown that reading material which allows for horizontal rather than vertical movement is of paramount importance. This series aims to provide such material in the form of stories, carefully selected for their appeal to children and for their significance in the traditions and cultures of the major world religions.

Stories from World Religions, obviously not a course in religious education, can usefully supplement the material in any agreed syllabus. While it emphasises Christianity as the religion that has shaped our national life, its aim is to introduce children to the major religions as the living beliefs of other peoples of our world.

Religious truth is conveyed as much through stories as through historical events. This series therefore aims to introduce children to the different kinds of story used in religion—myth, history, legend, parable, festival—and to help children to a progressive understanding of them so that they can apprehend the truths conveyed.

The controlled vocabulary and language structure have been carefully graded to make Book 1 most suitable for reading ages 7–8 years; Book 2 for 8–9 years; Book 3 for 9–10 years; and Book 4 for 10–11 years. This has been achieved by testing each story theoretically with a recognised readability analysis, and in practice by testing with children of the appropriate reading ages.

Norman J. Bull
Reginald J. Ferris

Contents

Stories in this Book   6

Symbols   10

Seven Days of Creation   14

All the Colours of the Rainbow   21

Symbols: Light   28

The Hermit who became King   30

Symbols: The Lotus Flower   39

The Boy who never Changed his Path   40

Symbols: The Wheel   47

The Lost Son   49

WIDE RANGE
Stories from World Religions

4

Norman J. Bull
Reginald J. Ferris

Oliver & Boyd

Illustrated by Sheila Galbraith, Jeremy Gower,
John Harrold, Tony Herbert, Nicholas Hewetson,
Michael Strand and Pat Tourret

OLIVER & BOYD
Robert Stevenson House
1–3 Baxter's Place
Leith Walk
Edinburgh EH1 3BB
A Division of Longman Group Ltd

First published 1983

ISBN 0 05 003373 5

Set in 12/16pt Plantin 110
Printed in Hong Kong by
Sheck Wah Tong Printing Press Ltd.

Symbols: The Swastika   61

Pilgrims to Mecca   63

Mahmud the Grumbler   76

Symbols: The Crescent   79

War Against Slavery   80

The Champion of Children   90

The Festival of Freedom   101

Symbols: The Star of David   110

Maundy Thursday   112

Symbols: The Cross   116

The Light of Life   118

Symbols: Yang and Yin   127

Stories in this Book

Everyone loves a story, and there are many different kinds of stories—from fairy tales to science fiction, from legends to biographies. Each story in this book tells us something about one of the great religions of the world, but the stories are not all of the same kind.

History

One kind of story in this book is about people who really lived, and about things that really happened. These real-life stories are called History, and they tell of people who lived and things that happened right up to the present day. History is full of stories about real people. Some of them are about people who became great, and famous, and loved.

Legends

People have always enjoyed hearing about their heroes in history, so other stories about heroes grew up too. These were not real-life stories. They were Legends. By exaggerating the truth, legends made a person seem even braver or stronger or better than he really was. So legends told of mighty wonders, great adventures, brave deeds, and fine actions. Although legends are told about men and women who are known to have really lived, we cannot be sure that the great deeds of which they tell really happened.

It is important for us to know whether a story is a legend or history, for both legends and history are used in the teachings of every religion. Legends are not just good stories: they are setting an example, to show us that we can be braver or better people.

Parables

Some stories are made up to help us to understand something that would otherwise be very difficult to grasp. Stories like these are called Parables.

By using a simple story from everyday life, each parable teaches us an important truth—either about God, about ourselves, or about each other. So in one sense stories like these, even though they are made up, are often far more important than stories from real life.

Myths

When we are young we are full of curiosity about our world and we ask many questions—how did the world begin, where did it come from, why is it here?

People in every land have traditional stories to explain how things began. These stories, called Myths, tell what people in the distant past believed about how things began and why they were made.

Although today we know much more about *how* things began from the discoveries of science, science cannot tell us *why* they began. Myths tell what people long ago *believed* about the world and why everything in it is the way that it is.

Festivals

Every year we have special times which we can share together; they are called Festivals.

Every religion has its festivals, and each festival has its own story of how it started. A festival is a time of remembering and celebrating things that happened long ago—things that are so important that people never want to forget them.

A festival story may be told in words, or acted in plays. It may be sung in carols, or brought to life in dance. The story of a festival explains the meaning of that festival and why it is important to people all over the world who share in it.

Different Kinds of Stories

So there are five kinds of stories in this book—History, Legends, Parables, Myths and Festival Stories—and they are all important in their different ways. Learn to recognise the difference between them—you will be able to understand and enjoy a story much more if you know what kind of story it is.

Symbols

Your name stands for YOU. When people are talking about you they use your name, because it means YOU. So it is what we call a symbol.

A symbol stands for something, just as your name stands for you. When you sign your name at the end of a letter, it means that YOU have said (and meant) all the words in that letter.

Numbers are symbols—special signs which tell us how many. Without them we could not count, or use money, or tell the time, or know the date. We are using number symbols all day long.

Symbols can be objects. When a man and a woman are married, the ring is a symbol of their marriage. The circular shape of a wedding ring is a symbol of eternity: it means "for ever". So a wedding ring is a symbol of a married couple's promise to love and care for each other for ever.

Colours are often used as symbols. Red stands for danger—we use it in traffic signs and in warning notices. In some countries, people wear black at a funeral as a sign of mourning and sorrow, and in other countries, white or blue are symbols of mourning.

Actions may be symbols. Many years ago, before there was much law and order, men carried tiny daggers in their hands to protect themselves or to be ready to stab an enemy. If a man wanted to be friends, he would offer an open, outstretched hand to show that he was not carrying a dagger. If the other man was also prepared to be friends, he would do the same, and they would then shake hands. Shaking hands is still a symbol of trust and friendship in many parts of the world.

There are many different kinds of religious symbols as well. They too can be signs, objects, colours or actions.

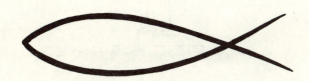

This very simple drawing of a fish was used by the early Christians as a secret sign. Only they knew what it stood for and what it meant. The Greek word for fish is ICTHUS, and the Christians made each letter of ICTHUS stand for a word, like this:

I   stood for Iesus, meaning JESUS
C   stood for Christos, meaning CHRIST
TH   stood for Theou, meaning OF GOD
U   stood for Uios, meaning SON
S   stood for Soter, meaning SAVIOUR

So, for Christians, the fish symbol meant JESUS CHRIST, SON OF GOD, SAVIOUR.

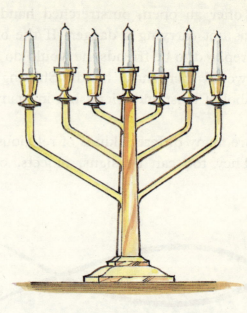

Here is a candlestick of a very particular shape, with seven branches. For Jews, it is an important symbol. It reminds them of the time when Moses took the Jews of old out of Egypt. They had to pass through the wilderness on their way to Canaan, the promised land. Since there were no holy places, God commanded Moses to build a movable holy place called a tabernacle, and furnish it. One of the things God commanded Moses to make was a golden candlestick with seven branches, and told him how it had to be decorated. So a candlestick of this kind stands in every Jewish synagogue, reminding Jews of their release from slavery long ago.

This Moslem is kneeling on his prayer-mat to worship Allah. Prayers are said five times each day. When they pray, Moslems face Mecca, where their sacred stone, the Kaaba, is kept. During the prayers, Moslems stand, bow, kneel, sit back on their heels, and touch the ground with their foreheads. All these actions are symbols of the Moslems' reverence for God.

As you read this book you will meet some of the many symbols which belong to the religions of our world. These symbols are very old. Each one stands for something important in a particular religion, and has a special meaning for those who follow that religion.

Seven Days of Creation

This story of how the world began comes at the very
beginning of the Bible of the Jews. Christians call it
the Old Testament, for they added to it their own
sacred writings, called the New Testament, to make
the Christian Bible. So both Jews and Christians share
this creation myth.

★   ★   ★   ★   ★   ★

In the beginning there was God.
It was he who created the heavens and the earth.
At first there was nothing but waters.
They had no shape, and there was no life in them.
They were covered with darkness.
Then the Spirit of God moved over the waters,
and God's work of creation had begun.
It was God's will to create all things.
He created by his word.
When he spoke, his will was done.
God said,
"Let there be light!"
and there was light.
God saw that the light was good,
and he separated the light from the darkness.
God called the light Day,

and the darkness he called Night.
Now there was evening and there was morning,
and this was the *first* day.
Then God said,
"Let there be a dome in the middle of the waters,
and let it divide the waters."
So God made the dome of the sky.
Its arch separated the waters under it
from the waters above it.
God called this dome Heaven.
There was evening and there was morning,
and this was the *second* day.
And God said,
"Let the waters under the heavens
be gathered together in one place,
and let dry land appear."
And it was so.
God called the dry land Earth.

The waters that were gathered together
he called Seas.
And God saw that it was good.
Then God said,
"Let the earth bring forth plants which give seeds
and trees which bear fruit with their seed,
each according to its kind."
And it was so.
The earth brought forth plants and trees
of all kinds.
And God saw that it was good.
There was evening and there was morning
and this was the *third* day.
God said,
"Let there be lights in the dome of heaven
to separate day from night.
Let them measure the seasons,
and the days, and the years.
Let them give light to the earth."
And it was so.

God made two great lights.
He made the greater light to rule the day,
and the lesser light to rule the night.
He also made the stars,
and set them in the dome of heaven.
They were to give light to the earth,
and to rule over day and night,
and to separate light from darkness.
And God saw that it was good.
There was evening and there was morning,
and this was the *fourth* day.
God said,
"Let the waters bring forth creatures
to live and move in them,
and let winged creatures fly above the earth
through the open sky."

So God created fish and sea creatures
to swim in the seas,
and birds to fly in the air,
each according to its kind.
And God saw that it was good.
Then God blessed all the creatures that he had made,
    saying,
"Let fish fill the waters of the sea.
Let birds flock together in the heavens."
There was evening and there was morning,
and this was the *fifth* day.
And God said,
"Let the earth bring forth living creatures of
    every kind—
cattle, and beasts of the field, and creeping things."
And it was so.

God made the beasts of the earth, and cattle,
and everything that creeps on the earth.
And God saw that it was good.
Then God said,
"Let us make man,
in our image, after our likeness.
Let man be lord of all other creatures—
the fish of the sea,
the birds of the air,
and everything that creeps on the earth."
So God created man in his own image,
in the likeness of God.
He made men and women.
And he blessed them, saying,
"I have made you lords of the fish of the sea,
the birds of the air,

19

and every living thing that moves on the earth.
I have given you plants and trees to provide your food,
and to feed the birds and beasts and creeping things."
And it was so.
And God saw everything that he had made,
and behold, it was very good.
There was evening and there was morning,
and this was the *sixth* day.
So the heavens and the earth were made.
God's work of creation was finished,
and on the *seventh* day God rested from his work.
So God blessed the seventh day, and made it holy.
It was hallowed for ever as a day of rest.
On the seventh day men should rest from their work,
just as God himself rested on the seventh day.

★　　★　　★　　★　　★　　★

This is more like a poem than a story. Jews used it in their worship of God at their Temple in Jerusalem, and they sang it during their New Year Festival, praising God for the wonders of his creation.

This story of the creation is very like the story believed long ago by the Babylonians. Today, science has given us many answers to questions about *how* the world came into being, and *how* living things developed, but it still has no answer to the question "Why?". This story was the early Jewish answer to the question "Why?".

All the Colours of the Rainbow

A rainbow can usually be seen on a sunny day when the sun is low in the sky, which means that morning or evening is the best time. To see it, stand with your back to the sun, and the rain clouds ahead of you.

We see the rainbow in the shape of a bow or an arch. An old legend says that treasure will be found at the places where the two ends of the bow touch the earth—"there's a pot of gold at the rainbow's end". But the rainbow does not really have two ends which touch the earth. It is a complete circle, not just part of a circle, and if you saw a rainbow from the top of a mountain or from an aeroplane, you would see the whole circle of colours.

Nowadays, a rainbow can help country people to tell what the weather is likely to be. They know that if they see a rainbow in broken pieces among the clouds, the weather is likely to be blustery and stormy. They know that if they see a rainbow in the evening, it is a good sign, for "a rainbow at night, the rain is gone quite". So to country people the rainbow is a sign telling of the weather that is to come.

★　　★　　★　　★　　★　　★

The rainbow was a much more important sign to people of long ago. They were terrified of times when the rain poured down without ceasing and flooded their land. The rainbow, when it came, was a sure and wonderful sign that the rains were over.

The rainbow was very mysterious to them. They could see it, but they could not touch it. Both the floods and the rainbow came from heaven, so they believed that the rainbow must have a heavenly meaning.

An ancient story of the Jews told how God had flooded the earth because of the wickedness of men and women. Only his good servant Noah and his family were saved from the floods by sheltering in the ark which they had made. The rainbow was God's sign to Noah that never again would he flood the earth. So, whenever Jews saw a rainbow, they remembered God's promise.

There are stories of floods among other peoples besides the Jews, and in these stories also the rainbow was believed to be a sign from heaven.

Some peoples believed that the rainbow was a living creature. The Greeks believed that it was a beautiful goddess named Iris who was the messenger of the gods. The Zulus of Africa had learnt to fear the huge poisonous snakes of their land. When they saw a rainbow in the sky they were filled with terror, for it reminded them of a serpent. The Aborigines of Australia, however, welcomed their rainbow serpent, with his red hair and his striped body. He was called Yero, and he gave the rain which watered the dry earth to make things grow.

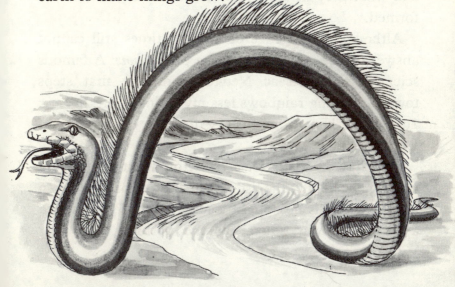

Some peoples believed that the rainbow was a bridge between heaven and earth. Gods and angels came down the rainbow bridge to visit people on earth, and the souls of the dead went up the bridge to heaven. In lands of the Norsemen, the rainbow bridge was named Bifrost. The souls of brave warriors who had died in battle were carried over Bifrost to win their reward in the heaven of Valhalla.

In the South Seas, people believed that when their heroes died, they climbed up the rainbow ladder to dwell in heaven.

*   *   *   *   *   *

These stories or *myths* of early times told what people believed about how things began, why they were made, and what they meant. They answered *why* a rainbow formed.

Although the science of modern times still cannot answer the question *why*, it can tell us *how*. A famous scientist called Isaac Newton took the first steps towards making rainbows less mysterious—in the year 1666, well known in history for the Great Fire of London.

One day in 1666 Isaac Newton went to the big trading fair held in the little town of Stourbridge. From one of the stalls he bought a solid piece of glass called a prism. It was square at the bottom, with four

triangular faces rising to a point at the top. He took it
back to his room in Cambridge, where he was a student
at Trinity College, and started to experiment with it
to find out more about light.

First of all he made the room dark by closing the
shutters over the windows. Then he made a tiny hole
in one shutter so that a beam of sunlight shone on to
the white wall. The beam of light was round, and it was
pure white. Then he put the glass prism in the line of
the beam, so that it had to pass through the glass. The
beam changed—it was no longer round. The glass
prism bent it into a long band, the shape of a semi-
circle. And it was no longer white. It was split up into
all the colours of the rainbow.

So white light went into the prism, and colours came out of it. Isaac Newton realised that this meant that white light must be made of all the colours joined together. The glass prism had separated them and spread them out. The violet at one end and the red at the other end both faded away into the darkness of the room.

He got a second prism and put it into the beam of light where the colours had been split up by the first prism. And just as he thought—the colours came out of the second prism as a single beam of white light once more. Isaac Newton had proved that sunlight is made of many different colours.

*　　*　　*　　*　　*　　*

What *are* these colours in light? First of all, the band of colours is called the spectrum, and the colours in it are always the same, and always in the same order.

Isaac Newton decided there were seven colours in light—red, orange, yellow, green, blue, indigo and violet. But there are really only five colours—he had made them into seven by separating violet and indigo from blue. So the five colours of the rainbow are red, orange, yellow, green and blue.

Light is made up of three main colours—red, green and blue—called the "primary" or first colours. All other colours can be made from these three colours, and white can be made by joining them together. These are the three colours used for spotlights in the theatre and in colour photography. They are also the colours used for colour television, the camera being really three cameras in one.

Although our eyes can distinguish only about a hundred and eighty different shades of colour, there are about eight thousand altogether. They all come from "the colours of the rainbow".

$$\ast \quad \ast \quad \ast \quad \ast \quad \ast \quad \ast$$

Isaac Newton had split up light into "all the colours of the rainbow" by using his glass prism, and if we think about this, we can understand how a rainbow happens.

We know that the colours come from the raindrops, because we often see the same thing happening when the sun shines on water spraying from a garden hose or from a fountain.

When white rays of sunlight fall on the drops of rain, each raindrop acts in just the same way as Isaac Newton's glass prism. The light is bent as it enters the raindrop, so that it splits into its separate colours. The rays of light, leaving the raindrops, are reflected back to earth. And we see a rainbow—an arch of colours from red at the top to violet-blue at the bottom.

We give meanings to colours. We use them as signs which tell us something. We should soon be in trouble if we did not know what red and green mean in traffic signs on our roads. Colours make fine symbols, too, which stand for something. We use them to make flags which stand for countries. In 1980 the new African country of Zimbabwe was formed. The colours used for its flag have special meanings—green stands for the country; gold for the minerals it contains; black and white for the people of different colours who live in it; red for the blood shed in order to get peace.

Symbols: Light

Light is a symbol in every religion—the greatest symbol of all. Light comes from the sun, and in early times men and women worshipped the sun itself as a God. In later times, people came to believe in other Gods, and light became a symbol of the Gods they worshipped.

Light stands for *life*. In the beginning there was only darkness; then God created light and the world came into being. Without light there would be no life, no living thing. So light is both a symbol of life and of the God who created it. Moslems say, "Allah is the Light of the heavens and of the earth."

Light stands for *truth*. Christians believe that Jesus is the "Light of the World", and that in him is the truth about all things.

Light stands for *goodness*, and its opposite, darkness, stands for evil. Many stories of creation say that in the beginning, light drove away darkness. In the same way, the goodness of God drives away the "powers of darkness".

Light stands for *knowledge*. When someone is said to have "seen the light", he knows and understands. Buddhists follow the teachings of Lord Buddha, whose name means "the wise one", or "the one who found the light".

Light shone from Gods and Prophets. It shone from holy men—a picture of a saint would show a halo of light round his head, which meant that he was holy. It was a symbol of the light that had come to him, bringing life, truth, goodness and knowledge.

The Hermit who became King

Lord Buddha, the Wise One, lived in India long, long ago. But still today, millions of people throughout the world follow his wise teachings.

One of the things Buddha taught was that each person has not just one life, but many lives. So a person may have lived on earth before, either as a human or as an animal. Each birth depends on his deeds in his last life: someone who has done evil may be reborn as an animal or as an insect; someone who has done good may be reborn as a higher person. So each Buddhist tries to lead a good life, in the hope that when he is born again, he will be higher and nobler.

Buddha said that before he was reborn as the Wise One, he had lived on earth many times. Buddhists love to hear stories about Buddha's different lives. They are called Jataka stories, for in India *jataka* means "birth".

Here is a Jataka story, told by Buddha, of how he had once lived on earth as a hermit (a holy man who lives alone so that he may be close to God).

*   *   *   *   *   *

In a city by the River Ganges, there once lived a prince named Devadatta. His name meant "Gift of God", but he was a horrible boy, and he grew into a horrible young man. He thought of no one but himself. He did as much harm as he could to everyone else. No wonder that everyone hated him, and called him "Prince Selfish".

It was the custom for the courtiers at the royal palace to go with the prince down to the sacred River Ganges, to bathe in its holy waters. One day while they were there, a fierce storm blew up, the rains poured down, and the river turned into a raging torrent. The courtiers saw their chance to get rid of the hateful prince. They seized Devadatta, hurled him far out into the angry waters and left him to drown.

Then they returned to the palace and told the king that the prince had been drowned. They said that he had insisted on going far out into the river ahead of them, and had disappeared from their sight. At once the king ordered a search to be made. It went on for days, but no trace of the prince was found, and the court went into mourning for his death.

★　　★　　★　　★　　★　　★

But Devadatta was not dead. He had managed to catch hold of a big log floating in the swollen river. He clung to it and it carried him far away. The selfish prince was not the only one to find safety by holding on to the log. A snake, a rat and a parrot were also clinging to it.

The snake was suffering for the evil he had done in his past life. He had been a king's treasurer, in charge of all the royal money. He had been dishonest, and over the years he had stolen the huge sum of thirty million pounds from his royal master. He had buried his treasure safely in a secret spot near the river.

It was just the same with the rat. He also had been the thieving treasurer of a great ruler. He too had a secret treasure of thirty million pounds hidden away in the earth by the river. Both Rat and Snake had been born as very lowly creatures because of their wickedness in their previous lives.

As all four—Snake, Rat, Parrot and Devadatta, the selfish prince—went hurtling down the river, they clung to the log for all they were worth, fighting for their lives.

Close by the river lived a hermit who, in a later life, was to come to earth as Buddha, the Wise One, although no one knew that then, of course. The holy man heard the cries of the prince and was filled with compassion. At once he left his simple cottage and hurried to the river bank. He saw the log rushing towards him with the prince and the three creatures clinging to it, and he waded quickly into the fast-flowing water. He just managed to reach the log with his hand and turned it so that it came towards the bank, where it was held fast. The kind hermit saw that the animals were weaker than Devadatta. He carried them first, one by one, to the safety of his cottage. Then he carried in the prince. He soon had the fire burning brightly and delicious soup warming in the pot.

Next the hermit looked after the animals, drying them and laying them gently by the fire. Only when this had been done did he help the prince to dry his clothes.

The hermit fed the animals first, too, so that they could recover their strength. Only when they had been fed did he give a bowl of hot soup to the hungry prince.

Devadatta was furious. "Wait till I get back to the palace!" he thought angrily to himself. "I'll soon have this wretched hermit arrested for his insults. Fancy putting animals before a prince! It will be a pleasure to see him suffer and die!"

The future Buddha cared for his guests until the

storm had died down and they were fully recovered. Devadatta was in a very bad temper. He strode off without a word of thanks to the hermit for saving his life. But the animals acted very differently.

Snake bowed respectfully to the holy man when he said goodbye. "Thank you for saving me, and for caring for me so kindly," he said. "I have a treasure hidden away, and if you ever need money, please come and ask me."

Rat too was full of gratitude to the hermit. He thanked him warmly, saying, "If you ever need money, please come and ask me."

Then Parrot thanked the holy man. "I do not have any money," he said, "but if you ever need the finest red rice, please come and ask me. I can call on the birds to help—we'd soon collect a full cartload for you."

So Snake, Rat and Parrot left the hermit's cottage and, like the prince, went back home. None of them knew that the kind hermit was to be the future Buddha.

★　　★　　★　　★　　★　　★

Some time later, the hermit decided to try out his new friends and put them to the test. First of all he went to the home of Snake and gently called him by name. Snake was delighted when he saw the kind hermit, and naturally thought that he had come for money.

"I'll take you to my treasure at once," he said. "You can have all the gold you want."

"No thank you," said the holy man. "I have no need of money just now. But if ever I do need some, I'll come to you again."

Then the hermit went to the home of Rat and gently called him by name. Rat too was delighted to see the kind holy man and, like Snake, thought he had come for money. "I'll take you to my treasure at once," he said. "You can have all the gold you want."

"No thank you," said the hermit. "I don't need your gold just now. But if ever I do, I'll come to you again."

Then the hermit went to the tree where Parrot lived and gently called him by name. At once Parrot flew down from his nest, high in the leafy branches. He was delighted that the kind hermit had accepted his offer of rice.

"I'll call my friends," said Parrot. "We'll soon collect a whole cartload of the finest red rice for you."

"No thank you," said the holy man. "I don't need any rice just now. But if ever I do, I'll come back to you again."

So Snake, Rat and Parrot were put to the test. All of them were eager to show their gratitude to the holy man for saving their lives, and all of them were eager to keep their promises.

Last of all, the hermit decided to call on the prince

who was now king. He went to the royal palace, and Devadatta saw him coming. At once he recognised the holy man who had insulted him by putting the animals first. He had forgotten all about him, but now he remembered, and decided to have his revenge. Quickly he called his servants.

"Arrest that man!" ordered Devadatta. "He is a dangerous enemy. Beat him without mercy, and take him to the place of execution. I want his head!"

The servants hurried to carry out the prince's orders. None of them had any idea that the man they had been told to kill would one day be the Buddha. They seized the hermit and dragged him away to the place of execution, beating him without mercy as they went.

There were some wise men standing by as the servants came along, dragging and beating the hermit.

The wise men found it strange that the prisoner did not try to defend himself. He made no sound. He did not cry with pain or shout with anger against the men who were ill-treating him.

"How meek that prisoner is!" they said to each other. "How brave he is!" They were so amazed that they stopped the servants and spoke kindly to the hermit.

"Why has the prince ordered his servants to treat you like this?" they asked him. "What is your crime? How have you offended Devadatta?"

Then the holy man told them of all that had happened when he had saved the prince and the three animals. The wise men were very angry and they spread the news all through the city. The people rose up in fury. They had stood enough of this evil prince and his wicked ways. They rebelled against him, attacked him and slew him. Then they crowned the hermit to rule over them in place of Devadatta.

So the future Buddha, filled with wisdom, love and compassion, ruled over the people and brought great happiness to his kingdom.

*　　*　　*　　*　　*　　*

It was not long before the new king went in state to visit his old friends, Snake, Rat and Parrot. How delighted they were to see the holy man in all his glory, surrounded by his courtiers. Now they could keep their promises to help the king provide for his people.

"You can have all my gold," said Snake gladly.

"You can have all *my* gold too," added Rat.

Parrot was not to be outdone by the others. The new king now had a huge treasure of sixty million pounds to provide for his people, but they would need food as well. Parrot and his friends brought the finest red rice to the royal palace every week—enough to feed the whole city.

The new king invited his three friends to come and live with him in the royal palace. They lived there for the rest of their days, and when they died, Snake, Rat and Parrot were reborn as nobles of the highest rank.

When the hermit's life as king was ended he had finished one more stage on the way to being born as Buddha, the Wise One.

Symbols: The Lotus Flower

The beautiful lotus flower has always been a popular symbol in lands of the East where it grows. The Indian lotus is a water lily with white flowers, each with eight petals. Its white petals look just like the sun's rays, and they open with the sun, too. At night, they close when the sun goes down. So the lotus became a symbol of the sun, and a symbol of life.

The pure white lotus grew out of waters that were dark and dirty with mud, and the lotus thrones of the Hindu Gods rise above the impure earth, just as the lotus holds its head above water.

This flower is specially sacred to Buddhists, whose stories tell of Buddha as being born from a lotus. Buddha is pictured as seated on a lotus, as if it were his throne. The eight petals of the Indian lotus symbolise the "Eight-Fold Path" taught by the Lord Buddha as the only way to the good life.

One of the holy writings of Buddhists is called the Lotus Scripture. It speaks of Buddha as the heart of the lotus flower, and its teaching is so precious to Buddhists that it is called The Jewel. From this comes the most popular prayer of Buddhists: "Hail to the Jewel in the Lotus!"

The Boy who never Changed his Path

Hindu people believe in Brahman which means "holy power". This divine spirit is in all things. Brahman is made known to Hindus in the Gods and Goddesses they worship. One of these is Lord Vishnu, the preserver of life. This story is about the kindly Vishnu whom many Hindus believe to be the greatest God of all.

*   *   *   *   *   *

Long ago, in the land of India, there lived a king who had two wives. His first wife was called Suniti, and she was quiet, gentle and kind. All she wanted was to make a happy and peaceful home for the king, whom she loved dearly. She bore him a son, and he was named Dhruva. Since he was the firstborn son, Dhruva would be king after his father.

The king's second wife was called Suruki. She was younger and more beautiful than Suniti, but she was proud and selfish, and she had a fierce temper. The king loved her for her beauty, and he gave her all she asked for. So Suruki ruled over him and over the whole royal palace. She even treated Queen Suniti like a servant, and gave her orders. She made sure that the king saw little of his first wife or of his firstborn son, Dhruva.

Suruki also bore him a son and, although he was not the king's firstborn son, she made up her mind that he, not Dhruva, would be the next king.

One day, when Dhruva was seven years old, both he and his young brother were with the king, who enjoyed playing with them. Dhruva was sitting on the king's lap when young Queen Suruki came into the room.

At once her temper flared up—she was furious because the king seemed to prefer Dhruva to her own son. She pulled Dhruva off the king's lap and shouted, "Go away! *My* son will be king, not you. *He* should be sitting on the king's knee! Go back to your ugly, stupid

41

mother!" Then she pushed Dhruva out of the room.

With tears streaming down his face, Dhruva went to his mother to be comforted. "Mother," he sobbed, "why can't I sit on my father's lap? Am I not his firstborn son? Won't I be king after him?"

Holding him in her arms, Queen Suniti tried to explain. "Dear Dhruva," she said sadly, "I am so sorry for you, but you see, Queen Suruki is so beautiful that your father always lets her have her own way."

"It's not fair!" said Dhruva, drying his eyes. "I know that my father has great power as king, and I know that Queen Suruki has power over him. But is there no one with even greater power? Someone who can make sure that people are treated fairly?"

"There is one," his mother said softly.

"Who is it?" cried Dhruva. "Tell me, and I'll go to him."

"It is Lord Vishnu, the great God who looks after us all. He is kind and just and fair."

"Where can I find him?" asked Dhruva eagerly.

"Lord Vishnu is everywhere," his mother answered. "But when he sees wrong being done, he comes to earth to put things right."

"Where can I go to look for him, Mother?"

"Perhaps he could be found in the depths of the forest," said Queen Suniti, trying to soothe Dhruva. She tucked him up in bed. "Sleep well, my son," she whispered, kissing him goodnight.

But Dhruva was not soothed, and he did not sleep. He believed what his mother had said. "I will go into the forest and find Lord Vishnu," he said to himself.

He waited till all was quiet in the palace. Then, at dead of night, he crept out and set off into the forest. It was like a jungle, thick with trees and bushes. It was the home of all kinds of living creatures, large and small, but Dhruva was not afraid. He was determined to go on till he found Lord Vishnu.

Soon after dawn broke, a huge bear lumbered on to his path.

"I'm looking for Lord Vishnu," said Dhruva politely. "Can you please tell me where to find him?"

The bear was astonished by the boy who stood in front of him and looked up at him without fear. He just shook his head in amazement and ambled off.

Not long after, a deer came leaping out of the trees and dashed past Dhruva. In hot pursuit came a fierce tiger. When the tiger saw the boy standing there, quite unafraid, he stopped in his tracks.

"I'm looking for Lord Vishnu," said Dhruva politely. "Can you please tell me where he is?"

The fierce tiger forgot all about the deer he was chasing and stood and stared at Dhruva. He was so surprised that he could not think what to do, and after a moment he ran off with his tail between his legs.

Dhruva plodded on. Some time later he met a lion who was roaring ferociously.

"I'm looking for Lord Vishnu," said Dhruva politely, showing no fear. "Have you seen him anywhere?"

The lion was so amazed that he stopped roaring. Indeed, he felt quite friendly to the brave boy who stood right under his nose. He just gave Dhruva a friendly lick, then leapt back into the jungle.

On and on went Dhruva, deeper and deeper into the forest. He was quite determined to find Lord Vishnu. He would never give up. He asked every creature he met, but none of them could help him. He was so determined that he did not think about eating or drinking or sleeping. Day after day he went on through the forest, searching for Lord Vishnu.

*　　*　　*　　*　　*　　*

Then one day, Dhruva came to a clearing in the forest. In the open space was a rough hut, the home of a hermit who had gone there to live alone, far away from people. The hermit was not pleased to see a human boy, but he felt sorry for Dhruva, who looked so thin and tired and hungry. What a strange boy he was, thought the hermit. Fancy searching for Lord Vishnu!

The hermit looked at Dhruva and then said, "Wash yourself in this pool of clear water. Then we'll eat together."

When they had finished eating, the hermit said, "If you want Lord Vishnu you must sit here, on this seat,

with your legs crossed under you. You must say 'I bow myself before Lord Vishnu', and you must say these words ninety million times. Then Lord Vishnu will surely come to you."

The hermit really wanted to get rid of Dhruva so that he could be alone again. "The boy will soon get tired of saying that," the hermit thought to himself. "Then he'll go back and leave me in peace."

But Dhruva did just as the hermit had told him. He sat there, saying over and over again, "I bow myself before Lord Vishnu." Without food, he grew thinner and thinner. Without sleep, he grew more and more tired. But he would not give up. He was determined to find Lord Vishnu.

And so it was that Lord Vishnu himself took pity on Dhruva. The great God came to earth and carried the boy up to the heavens. There, in the heavens, he gave Dhruva his own place—and the boy Dhruva became Dhruva, the Pole Star.

As time went by, men discovered that Dhruva the Pole Star did not change its position as other stars did. It stands almost directly above the North Pole. Famous seamen of ancient times found that the Pole Star could guide them on their travels, and could lead them on their voyages of discovery. For hundreds of years, all sailors depended on the Pole Star to guide them on their voyages, for Dhruva the Pole Star, like Dhruva the boy, would never change its path.

Symbols: The Wheel

The wheel has always been a fine symbol of the sun. The sun is the hub at the centre of the wheel, and the spokes are the sun's rays. The wheel is also used as a symbol of time, for time rolls by, just as a wheel rolls on.

To the people of Tibet, the wheel is a symbol of life. Their Wheel of Life has three animals in the centre: a cock, which stands for pride; a snake, which stands for hate; and a pig, which stands for greed. Tibetans believe that these are the three worst evils of all.

Hindus believe in the Wheel of Karma—the "Wheel of Doing". They believe that a person has many lives, not just one life. People who follow the Buddhist religion also hold these beliefs. How a person is reborn depends on the deeds he or she has done in the previous life. If those deeds were evil, the person may be reborn as an animal or an insect, in a lower form of life. If the deeds were good, the person may be reborn as a finer and purer person.

Buddhists and Hindus believe that the soul never dies. When it is perfect it will go to heaven, but until then it must go through many lives. They believe that every person is bound to the Wheel of Doing, and no one can escape the results of his or her deeds, whether good or bad.

Each religion shows that the only way to escape from the Wheel of Doing is by living better and better lives so that in the end the soul becomes perfect and goes to heaven.

The Lost Son

Jesus told this famous parable. He wanted people to understand that God's love for all his children never changes, just like the father's love for his children in this story, no matter how badly they have behaved.

    ★   ★   ★   ★   ★   ★

Joshua was a happy man. He had a big farm, for he had worked hard all his life, and he had two sons whom he loved dearly. He hoped that soon they would marry and have children of their own to bring joy to him in his old age. Through them his family would go on, and his name would be remembered in years to come. How happy Joshua was as he looked out over his fields, his orchards and his vineyards.

His happiness was not to last, however. His two

sons, Simon and John, were very different from each other. Simon, the elder son, was content to be a farmer and to work long days in the fields. John, on the other hand, thought that life on the farm was dreary. He was bored because nothing ever seemed to happen there, and he longed to get away and see the world. He had heard of Greek and Roman cities across the River Jordan, where exciting things were happening and life was full of fun. That was the kind of life he was looking for. He knew that he had nothing to look forward to at home, for his brother, as the eldest son, would inherit the farm and continue his father's family. John, as the younger son, would have to make his own way in the world.

As time went by, he grew more and more restless. "I'm eighteen years old—I'm a man now," he said to himself. "It's time I left home." Then he had an idea. He knew that by law Simon would inherit two-thirds of their father's wealth, but as he was the only other child, the other third would be all his when his father died. "I'll ask father for my share now!" John decided. "After all, it will come to me sooner or later. Then I'll use the money to go abroad and start a business of my own. I'll show them how clever I am!"

He went straight to his father. "Father, I want to have my share of your money now. I would like to travel, and make my own living. I know I can do well, and make you proud of me!"

At this, all Joshua's happiness left him and he was filled with sorrow. Not because of the money—that was not important—but because he knew that he might never see John again. Joshua did not feel it was right, however, to stand in his son's way, so he sold off some of his land to raise the money.

John was impatient to be gone. As soon as he was given his bag of gold, he quickly said goodbye and hurried off. Tears filled Joshua's eyes and his heart was heavy as he watched his beloved son disappear into the distance.

★   ★   ★   ★   ★   ★

John was in high spirits when he came to the beautiful town of Jerash, on the other side of the River Jordan. It had been built by the Greeks, and made even finer by the Romans. Even today we can see from its ruins what a wonderful city it must have been.

John had the sense to put his gold in the bank straightaway. He knew he would be able to draw out money whenever he wanted some to spend, and in the meantime the gold would be safe and it would be earning interest.

Next, he fitted himself out with fine new clothes which he bought from the splendid shops in Jerash. Then he began to enjoy himself. He went to the hippodrome to see the horse racing. He went to the

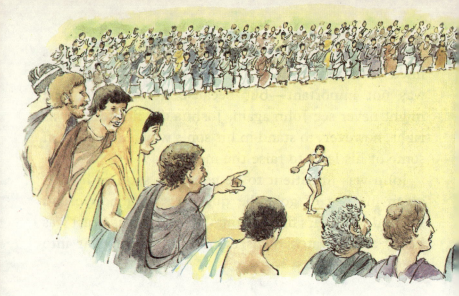

stadium to watch the Greek athletes competing in their sports and games. He went to the theatre to enjoy the plays which were presented by great actors. He found plenty of new friends, too, for the rich young Jew, with money to spend, soon became very popular.

Every day there was music and dancing, drinking and feasting, with these new-found friends. "This is the life I wanted!" John said to himself happily.

Jerash was full of grand temples to the Gods and Goddesses of the Greeks and Romans. As a Jew, John had been brought up to worship the one true God, and to have nothing to do with any other Gods. According to Jews, the Gods and Goddesses of Jerash were heathen idols, and the people who worshipped them were ignorant pagans, but John did not think about religion at all. He was glad to be free from the

religion of his people and their strict laws for living. Indeed, since he was wearing Greek clothes and living by Greek customs, he began to feel that he had been living in Jerash all his life!

John was so busy enjoying himself that the idea of starting a business and making his living faded from his mind. He thought there was no hurry, for he had plenty of money in the bank.

A day came, however, when the bankers told him that he had no more money left. He had spent every penny he had been given by his father!

At once John thought of his friends. "I need not worry," he said to himself. "I have many friends and they will look after me." John was mistaken, however. His so-called friends had been "fair-weather" friends: only his father's money had bought their friendship.

All his money was spent, so his friends had gone too.

John was all alone—a penniless stranger in a strange land.

★   ★   ★   ★   ★   ★

John did not find it easy when he started to look for work to earn money for food. There was a famine in the land and times were hard.

He decided to go out into the countryside, for he knew a lot about farming and he was sure he would soon get a job on the land. John tried to find work first at one farm, then at another, but no one had a job for the ragged beggar he had become.

At last a pig-farmer took pity on him, and gave him a job as a swineherd, looking after pigs. It was the lowest job of all for anyone, but what was even worse, pigs were regarded as unclean animals in the sacred laws of the Jews. Greeks and Romans were fond of pork meat from pigs. Worse still, they used pigs as sacrifices to their Gods and Goddesses. No good-living Jew would ever have anything to do with pigs. In becoming a swineherd, John was going against the religion of his people. He had no choice, however—he had to eat to keep himself alive, and he needed money to buy food. So he had to take whatever job he could find, and this was the only one.

There were times when he was even glad to eat the

pigs' food, he was so hungry. The pigs were given rough beans to fatten them up for market—John hated those beans, but at least they filled his empty, aching stomach.

As he sat in his filthy rags alone with the pigs, John had plenty of time to think. "What a fool I've been!" he said to himself. "I was far better off at home. I had everything I needed on the farm, and as my father's son, everyone respected me. Look at me now—I have no food, no shelter, no clothes, no money, no friends— nothing! Why, even my father's servants are better off than I am!"

As he went on thinking, John decided what he would do. "I will go back home," he said to himself. "I'll go back to my father and tell him that I've sinned against God and against him, too. Since I've had my share of his money, I have no claim on him at all. So I can't expect him to take me back as his son—or even as a servant of the family. I shall ask him to let me be one of the common labourers on his farm. I'll say to him, 'Father, I'm not fit to be treated as your son. Please take me on as a hired worker in your fields'."

★   ★   ★   ★   ★   ★

It was a long, hard journey back home. John looked like a dirty, tattered beggar as he hobbled along the rough stony tracks, living on scraps and sleeping by the roadside. No one would have recognised him as the smart son of Farmer Joshua who had left home so proudly to make his way in the world.

But there was one person who did recognise him —his father. When John had left home, Joshua had been broken-hearted. Every day after that he had gone up the steps on the outside of the farmhouse, and on to the flat roof. There he had sat, day after day, watching, waiting, longing for his dear son to come home. When he saw the ragged beggar hobbling towards the farm, he knew at once it was John. At last his lost son was returning to him!

Joshua hurried from the roof. He ran down the road, and clasped John in his arms, crying aloud with joy and weeping tears of happiness. John could hardly speak as his father hugged and kissed him. He tried to say the special words he had planned: "Father, I have sinned against God and against you. I am not fit to be called your son. Please let me stay and work as one of your hired labourers."

But his father did not hear a single word. Joshua was busy clapping his hands and shouting for his servants. "My son has come home!" he cried, as they hurried out. "Quick! Fetch my best robe to honour him as my son! Bring one of my gold rings for his finger, so that everyone will know he has my authority! Bring

sandals for him, too! We can't have him going round
with bare feet like the servants." Then he said to the
steward of his household, "Prepare a feast! Kill the
fatted calf which we have been keeping for a great
festival! We must eat and drink and be merry! For my
son was dead to me—and now he is alive again! He
was lost, and now he is found!"

*   *   *   *   *   *

What a feast they had when all the relatives and friends
had gathered together! There was the music of flutes
and pipes, drums and tambourines, with everyone
joining in the round dance. There was singing,
stamping of feet and clapping of hands. The sound of
such merrymaking could be heard from a long way off.

And someone did hear it—Simon, the elder son of
Joshua, trudging back home after a long, hard day in
the fields. He called out to a servant, "What is all that
noise? Why is there such merrymaking?" The servant
told Simon that his brother John had returned home,
safe and sound, and that his father had ordered a feast
to celebrate his homecoming. Simon was furious when
he heard this news.

The servant went to tell Joshua that Simon had
returned from the fields. "Run back to him quickly!"
said Joshua. "Ask him to join us and take his place
of honour at our feast!"

"What!" shouted Simon, when the servant gave him his father's message. "Does he think I'm going to make merry just because that lazy good-for-nothing fellow has come back? I'm not going in—and you can tell him so!"

Then Joshua himself came out to plead with Simon. He began to speak kind and loving words, but Simon interrupted him. He shouted at his father in his rage.

"All these years I've slaved on your farm!" cried Simon. "I've always obeyed you! I've served you faithfully, but you have never given me even so much as a lamb to make merry with my friends! Yet when that layabout son of yours comes back after wasting your money with the riff-raff of the town, nothing is too good for him! The fatted calf is killed for him, and a grand feast is prepared!"

Farmer Joshua loved Simon just as he loved John. He understood how Simon felt, and why he was angry. So he did not speak sternly to his eldest son for such rudeness. He did not tell Simon that he had done no more than his duty by working on the farm. He did not point out that Simon was really working for himself, because the farm would belong to him one day anyway. Nor did he mention that Simon could have had a feast at any time he wished.

Although Joshua understood Simon's feelings, he was saddened by his son's bitter and unforgiving heart. He knew that if it had been up to Simon he would have turned John away and rejected him, as the law allowed. Most fathers would have done so, too, but not Joshua. His love for his children was like the love of the heavenly Father for all his children.

"Simon, my dear, dear son," he said gently. "You are always with me; I know I can always rely on you. All that I have is yours, you know that. But John is my son too—and I love you both. It makes me happy just to have you both with me. When John left home, I was afraid I would never see him again. He was dead to me —and now he's alive again. He was lost to me—and now he is found. It was right that we should celebrate. Come in with me, my son. Come and share my joy. Then my happiness will be complete."

Symbols: The Swastika

The swastika is one of the oldest symbols of all, and it is a type of cross. It has been used for four thousand years. It is found in many parts of the world, and in many religions.

The word swastika comes from the ancient language of India used for holy writings, and it means "It is well". The swastika always stood for good—good luck, good fortune, good wishes, blessings.

The shape of the swastika stood for the sun and its rays. It was sometimes called the Sun Wheel, and it was often shown with the sun.

The Hindus of India used the swastika as a symbol of their Gods, and the Indians of America also used it as a symbol.

Ancient pictures of Buddha show him with a swastika on his breast. It stood for the heart of Buddha, and for his wisdom and teaching. The swastika was sometimes called the Buddhist Cross.

Christians at Rome buried the dead in underground passages called catacombs. It could be dangerous for them to declare their belief openly, so they often carved a swastika on the tomb of a Christian who died. It was a secret symbol of the Cross on which Jesus died. In later times, the swastika stood for Matthew, Mark, Luke and John, the writers of the four gospels, with Jesus at the centre.

In modern times the swastika was used by Hitler, leader of Germany from 1933 to 1945. He used it as a symbol of his evil beliefs. Although this has made the swastika an evil symbol, its true meaning has always been good.

Pilgrims to Mecca

Mecca in Arabia is the holy city of the Moslems, people who follow the religion of Islam. This story tells why Mecca became their holy city, and how they go there as pilgrims.

*　　*　　*　　*　　*　　*

In the year 570 a boy named Mohammed was born in a town called Mecca, in the desert land of Arabia. His father died before he was born, and his mother died when he was six years old. At first, his grandfather took care of him. Later, the boy was looked after by an uncle. Mohammed always remembered what it was like to be an orphan, and he never forgot the kindness of the relatives who had cared for him.

Mecca was an important town, for it lay on the trade route to far-off India. Trading was done by merchants who travelled on camels, sometimes called the ships of the desert. Groups of merchants and their camels rested at Mecca before setting off to the East. Such groups were called caravans, and they took with them silver and skins and dried fruits. They came back with precious things from the lands of the East—gold and cloth, rare spices and costly perfumes.

The traders of Mecca grew rich from the caravans. Mohammed's uncle was a busy tradesman and he often

took the boy with him on his journeys.

When Mohammed grew up, he worked and travelled with the camels on the caravans. Because he was honest, hard-working and trustworthy, he was made the caravan leader for a rich lady named Khadijah. Before long Mohammed married Khadijah. They were very happy, and they had six children.

Mohammed went on working hard, and in time he became one of the richest merchants in Mecca.

* * * * * *

To the Arabs, the city of Mecca was famous as a holy city. It had a sacred building called the Kaaba, built in the shape of a cube. In one wall of the Kaaba there was a sacred stone. It was thought to be a meteorite

which had fallen from the sky and had been blackened by heat as it fell to earth. Arabs believed that the Black Stone had been sent by God. Their wandering tribes came from all over Arabia as pilgrims to Mecca. There they went to the Kaaba to kiss the holy Black Stone which had come to them from God. Nearby was a holy well. It was called Zamzam from the noise made by the water as it oozed out. To the Arabs, the water from the sacred well was also holy.

But Mecca was not a holy city to Mohammed. On his travels with the caravans he had met many people. He had met Jews and Christians who both believed in one God, the Creator and Lord of all. He had heard from Jews how God had made himself known to them through messengers called Prophets. He had heard from Christians how Jesus had made God known to them through his teaching. Mohammed knew that both Jews and Christians had a holy book which told them about God. It also told them that they should love and respect one another and live together in peace.

Life in the holy city of Mecca was very different from all these teachings. The Kaaba was filled with hundreds of idols, worshipped by the Arab tribes. Many people of Mecca grew rich from all the pilgrims, but they cared for no one but themselves. They did not care for the poor, they were cruel to women and to slaves, and they cheated in their trading to make themselves even richer.

Mohammed liked to be alone, and he often went out into the desert by himself. It was there, when he was forty years old, that he began to see visions. In a dream, Gabriel—the angel of God—appeared to him, holding out a silk cloth with writing on it.

"Recite these words!" cried the angel.

"But I cannot read," stammered Mohammed.

"Recite!" the angel said again.

Then Mohammed began to recite, and the words of God were printed on his memory. Then the angel said to him, "Mohammed, I am Gabriel, the angel of God. You are the Messenger of God."

Mohammed was troubled by his dream, because he did not feel he was worthy of such a great calling. But his wife Khadijah believed that he *was* worthy. In time, Mohammed also came to believe that God had called him to be his Messenger or Prophet, and that he was worthy of his calling.

God's message was clear: There is only one true God. He is Allah (which in Arabic means "The God"). Allah is great, wise and powerful, the King and Judge of all. But he is compassionate and merciful as well. The duty of men and women is to submit to Allah, to surrender to him, and to seek his compassion and mercy. God will also be a stern Judge in the life to come. Those who have submitted to him, and have lived by his laws, shall dwell for ever in the Garden of Paradise. But for those who have not submitted, the Day of Judgement will bring the punishment of hell.

*   *   *   *   *   *

Mohammed began to proclaim God's message to the rich people of Mecca. He told them that God condemned their idols, their dishonesty in trading, their neglect of the poor, and their cruelty to women and slaves. At first the rich people laughed at Mohammed and mocked him. Then they grew angry. They knew that if they gave up all their idols, they would lose the wealth which came to them from the pilgrims. They began to attack Mohammed and his followers.

In the year 622, Mohammed left Mecca and went to an oasis in the north. There he was welcomed, and the oasis came to be called Medina—City of the Prophet. There Mohammed went on proclaiming his message from God, and there the religion of Islam began. Islam means "submission", and Mohammed's followers came to be called "Moslems", which means "those who have submitted" to the will of Allah.

Mohammed had to lead his Moslems into battle to defend his faith against enemies from Mecca. More tribes of Arabs accepted him as their leader, and more Arabs became Moslems. Soon Mohammed had enough followers to return to Mecca, and in the year 630 he entered the city in triumph. The Moslems smashed all the idols in the Kaaba, shouting aloud, "There is no God but Allah, and Mohammed is his Messenger!"

Mohammed made Mecca the true holy city of Moslems, and the Kaaba became the holy place of Allah.

*　　*　　*　　*　　*　　*

In the year 632, Mohammed died, but other leaders were chosen to be his Caliphs or Successors. Moslem armies and Moslem traders carried the religion of Islam from Arabia to other countries. Within a hundred years, Moslems had spread their faith from Spain in the West to China in the Far East, and down into Africa.

Today the religion of Islam stretches right across Africa and Asia. In these Moslem lands there are over nine hundred million people who follow the religion founded by Mohammed. Moslems in all these lands share five great beliefs, called the Five Pillars of Islam. They come from the holy book of Moslems called the Koran, which means the Recitation. The Koran contains the heavenly words which came to Mohammed in his visions. Mohammed could not read or write, so he recited them to his followers. Soon after his death, the words were written down and became the Koran. Moslems believe that the Koran is the Word of God, given to them by his Messenger Mohammed.

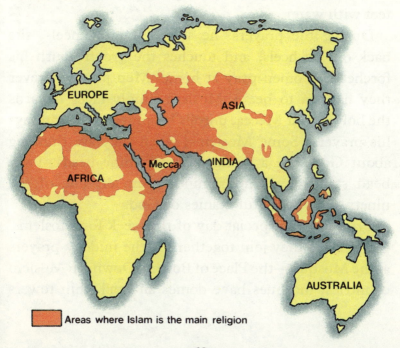

Areas where Islam is the main religion

The first Pillar of Islam is belief in one Almighty God: "There is no God but Allah and Mohammed is his Messenger!" This belief is recited five times every day by Moslems. It is whispered into the ears of a newborn child. It is chanted by mourners when they bury the dead.

*　　*　　*　　*　　*　　*

The second Pillar is the worship of God, five times each day—at dawn, midday, afternoon, evening and night. Each time there is the same order of prayers from the Koran to be recited. A Moslem prepares for the time of worship by washing his head and hands and feet with water.

During the prayers, he stands, bows, kneels, sits back on his heels, and touches the ground with his forehead. Women pray at home. Men pray wherever they happen to be. A Moslem simply faces towards the holy city of Mecca, unrolls his prayer mat, and says his prayers. Some Moslems, when they are thinking about God, use a string of ninety-nine beads. Each bead stands for, and reminds them of, one of the ninety-nine Beautiful Names of God.

Friday is the special day of the week for Moslems. On Fridays they join together for the midday prayers at the Mosque—the Place of Bowing Down. In Moslem countries, mosques have domes and tall, thin towers

called minarets. At the times of worship a voice calls loudly from a minaret: "God is most great. There is no God but God. Mohammed is the Messenger of God. Come to prayer."

At the midday prayers on Friday, there may be a sermon as well as prayers, but when the service is over, the men go back to work. Although Friday is a special day to the Moslems, it is not a day of rest as the Sabbath is for Jews and Sunday is for Christians.

*   *   *   *   *   *

The third Pillar of Islam is Almsgiving, which means giving money to the poor. Mohammed had made it a duty for Moslems to give a fixed part of their incomes to the poor and needy. He never forgot that he himself had been a poor orphan, depending on the kindness and generosity of others.

*　　*　　*　　*　　*　　*

The fourth Pillar is the month of fasting called Ramadan. During the fast, Moslems remember the time when Mohammed had his first vision and was given the words of God. Ramadan is a time of strict discipline when all Moslems in good health must go without food or drink during the hours of daylight.

The month of Ramadan ends with a joyful Festival of Fast-breaking—a happy time of holidays, visiting friends, giving presents, feasting and letting off fireworks. There is a strict rule that no one should fast during this happy festival. Moslems think, however,

that the finest way of celebrating the end of Ramadan is to give to the poor.

★ ★ ★ ★ ★ ★

The fifth Pillar of Islam is making a journey to the holy city of Mecca as a pilgrim. Every Moslem is expected to go to Mecca once during his lifetime, if he is healthy and can afford the journey. Some Moslems save money all their lives so that they can go to Mecca during the month of pilgrimage. When a Moslem has made the pilgrimage, he can proudly add the name "Al-Hajji" to his other names.

To make the pilgrimage to Mecca, all pilgrims go bare-footed. Women have their heads covered and wear a long white garment. Men are bare-headed and

wear simply two white sheets covering the upper and lower parts of the body. Moslems believe that they are all equal in the sight of God, and that all Moslems are brothers. So the pilgrims dress alike to make sure there are no differences of money, class, colour or country.

Pilgrims keep many sacred customs at Mecca during the days of pilgrimage. The most sacred of all is to pass seven times around the Kaaba, to bow to the sacred Black Stone and to touch it or to kiss it.

Some pilgrims go on to Medina, to honour the tomb of Mohammed and to pray in the mosque which he helped to build there. Some take home sacred water from the holy well of Zamzam. Very old pilgrims, after saving money all their lives to go to Mecca, would be happy to die there, because it is the most sacred place on earth in their religion.

There are over three hundred thousand Moslems at Mecca during the month of pilgrimage, and they live in a forest of tents. Once they travelled on camels or on foot, but now many pilgrims come by car. Many also come by air, landing at Jeddah, the airport for Mecca. The great Holy Mosque can hold all the pilgrims. Many new mosques and centres for pilgrims, and car parks too, have been made in recent times.

The land around Mecca and Medina is holy ground to Moslems. There are stone monuments at the borders, and only Moslems are allowed to enter. Any stranger to Islam who entered this holy land would be in danger of punishment by death.

Moslem children are taught the Koran in their schools and learn passages from it by heart in the Arabic language. It teaches them how to worship God and how to live together in the religion of Islam. Islam has few special ceremonies, and no priests. It has no special day of rest. In its beautiful mosques, Moslems simply kneel and pray to Allah. They face the holy city of Mecca and recite the sacred words of the Koran—the Word of God which came to them through Mohammed, the Messenger of God.

Mahmud the Grumbler

Every religion has its parables—stories of everyday
life but with a deeper meaning—like the ones Jesus
told. Here is a Moslem parable, from the Islamic
religion.

★   ★   ★   ★   ★   ★

In the land of Persia there once lived a man named
Mahmud. He was a good Moslem, and every day he
said his prayers to Allah at the appointed times. Each
Friday, at midday, it was the duty of Moslems to go
to the mosque and to join together in the worship of
Allah. Mahmud looked forward to the service on
Fridays, and he was always there.

It is the custom for Moslems to take off their shoes
before going into the mosque, and to leave them
outside. Some men have grand shoes and some have
plain shoes. Some men even have worn-out shoes—but
that does not really matter, because it is by taking *off*
their shoes that they show their reverence for the holy
place of Allah.

One Friday, Mahmud was very upset, because he
had no shoes to wear. His old shoes were in pieces
and he had no money to buy new ones. He tried to
borrow shoes from his friends, but they were all going

to the mosque that week themselves. There was nothing for it—Mahmud would have to go to the mosque in his bare feet, and he would have no shoes to leave outside.

Mahmud was always grumbling, and that Friday he grumbled to himself all the way to the mosque. "What a poor wretch I am!" he moaned. "What a hard life I have! I can't even afford a pair of shoes!"

He felt even worse when he saw the rows of shoes outside the mosque. People were admiring the grand shoes which rich men were proudly taking off. "It's not fair!" Mahmud went on grumbling to himself. "Why should they be so rich and me so poor? Why should Allah bless them and not me?"

As he went into the mosque, Mahmud was still grumbling to himself. He knelt down and bowed to the ground, and tried to join in the prayers, but he was not in the right mood for praying. He looked round at other worshippers, wondering what kind of shoes *they* had, and feeling so sorry for himself that he had no time to think about Allah. Suddenly his glance fell on the man kneeling in front of him, and Mahmud realised he could not see his feet. He thought at first they must be hidden under the man's garment. Then the awful truth came to him—the poor man had no feet.

It was a terrible shock to Mahmud. It made him realise his own selfishness and he felt deeply ashamed. He had been grumbling because he had no shoes—but here was a man who had no feet.

As he walked home from the mosque in his bare feet, Mahmud was a new man. All his bitterness and envy were gone, and his heart was full of thankfulness to Allah for all his blessings. For the first time in his life Mahmud realised that although he was poor, there were people who were far worse off than he was. He had so much to be thankful for, so much to make him happy and content. Never again would he grumble. Never again would he feel sorry for himself. The crippled man had taught Mahmud a lesson that he would never forget.

From that day on, everyone was amazed at the change in Mahmud. Suddenly the grumbler had become a happy man, counting his blessings instead of his troubles. Mahmud told them why he had changed so much, and his story spread.

And that was how the people of Persia got one of their wisest sayings: "I grumbled because I had no shoes—until I met a man who had no feet."

Symbols: The Crescent

The crescent, originally associated with moon worship, is a symbol which is used widely in the Middle East.

The moon is crescent-shaped when it is waxing or growing, so the crescent can stand for growing power. There is an Arab legend which tells how a Sultan named Othman had a vision. The vision showed a crescent moon which grew and grew until its horns stretched over the whole world from East to West. The Sultan wanted his religion to spread far and wide in this way, so he made the crescent the symbol of his people, the Turks. In time, it also became the symbol of the religion of Islam and of all Moslems.

That is why the crescent is often used for the flags of Moslem countries. Sometimes stars appear with the crescent. It is usually shown as a white crescent, but it is also shown in red as the symbol of the Red Crescent, which is the Moslem equivalent of the Red Cross organisation.

War Against Slavery

Today we think it horrifying that men and women and children should be bought and sold as slaves. But once there were slaves in Britain, and it is only about a hundred and fifty years since a law was passed to free all slaves in British lands. This is the story of two Christian men who fought to stop the terrible trade in human beings.

*   *   *   *   *   *

Early in the year 1760, a young man was walking cheerfully through the streets of London. His name was Granville Sharp and he was going to visit his brother, who was a doctor. When he reached his brother's house, he was horrified to find a poor negro lying on the doorstep. The man's body was thin and covered with sores, and he was shaking with fever. Granville Sharp carried the black man into the house, and his brother attended to him.

When the man was better, he told the two brothers his story. "My name is Jonathan Strong," he began. "My home was in Africa, where chiefs among my black people seize men of other tribes and sell them to white men in exchange for guns and strong drink. Me and some of my friends were seized and chained

together, then we were taken to the white men's settlement on the coast. Those who fell ill were left to die by the wayside. At the coast the white men chained us in their slave ship with many other negroes, and the ship sailed over the sea to America. Many of us fell ill, and those who died were thrown overboard. When we reached the West Indies, the strong men were sold for sixty pounds each. Weak men were sold with the women and children—for much less."

Granville Sharp had never in his life heard such a terrible story. He knew at once that he was going to have to do something about this dreadful human suffering, but first he would have to find out all he could about it. "What did you do in the West Indies?" he asked Jonathan.

"We were made to work very hard on the sugar plantations, but after being chained up for weeks in the ship, none of us were fit. Many fell ill and died, and in the end, only about half of us were left."

Granville Sharp clenched his fists. "We must stop this wickedness!" he cried.

"Not all of us suffered so badly," said the negro, trying to calm him. "Some slaves are treated well by their masters, and sometimes they are allowed to marry. If slaves work very hard, and please their masters well, they may even earn their freedom."

"That makes it worse!" cried Granville Sharp. "No man can own another man. We are all the children of God. He made us free and everyone is precious to him, black or white. To buy or sell a human being is worse than a crime against man. It is a sin against God!"

*   *   *   *   *   *

Jonathan Strong went on to tell how his master had brought him to England as a servant. He had been a cruel master. He had beaten Jonathan and starved him, and when the slave had become too ill to work, his master had thrown him out into the street. It was then that Granville Sharp had found him.

The two brothers looked after Jonathan till he was well again, then they found a good home for him.

But one day Jonathan's old master recognised him

in the street. "Why, there's my old slave," he said to himself. "He looks fit and able to work. After all, he *is* my property—I should get a good price for him."

So Jonathan was seized by his old master and sold to a planter for thirty pounds. Granville Sharp was very angry when he heard what had happened. Quickly he brought the matter before the law court of the Lord Mayor of London. Both Jonathan's old master and his new owner claimed him as their property.

"The slave has done nothing wrong," said the Lord Mayor. "He must be set free." So Jonathan was taken off the slave ship which was waiting to take slaves to the West Indies. This time he had been saved, but as a black man he would never be free from danger.

Granville Sharp looked for other negro slaves, and when he found them, he took their cases to court. But there was no clear law against slavery in England. Nor could he find a lawyer who would help him. So, for two whole years, Granville Sharp studied books of law to prepare himself for his fight against slavery.

He learnt everything he could about the slave trade, as well. He found that half the trade in buying and selling slaves was done by Britain. Each year, a hundred thousand black people were taken from Africa to America in British ships to be sold as slaves. By the time that Granville Sharp took up the fight, there were two million slaves owned by British planters in America, toiling in plantations there.

When the planters grew rich they came back to England. They brought slaves with them to be servants in their fine houses. There were fifteen thousand black slaves in Britain, and they were often offered for sale in newspaper advertisements. There were two hundred slave ships using the ports of London, Liverpool and Bristol. These ships flew the British flag, and had slaves chained in their holds.

The Public Advertiser
28th November, 1769

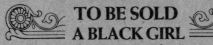 **TO BE SOLD**
A BLACK GIRL
eleven years of age,
Extremely handy, Works at her needle tolerably,
Speaks English perfectly well,
Is of an excellent temper, and willing disposition.
Inquire of: Mr. Owen, The Angel Inn,
Behind St. Clement's Church,
The Strand,
London.

At last Granville Sharp decided he was ready for the fight. He knew the law, and he knew all about the slave trade. He argued in court, but none of the judges would say that slavery was against the law. Then in 1772, the Lord Chief Justice of England himself was forced to hear a case about a slave. For five long months, Granville Sharp argued from the law books and gave evidence about the evils of slavery.

Then the Lord Chief Justice made up his mind, and gave his decision. "No one can be a slave in Britain," was his judgement. "The moment a slave sets foot on British soil, he becomes a free man."

*   *   *   *   *   *

Granville Sharp had won a great victory. Every slave in Britain was now a free man. But this was only the beginning. The war had to go on—against the slave trade in British ships, and against slavery in the British Colonies.

Granville Sharp knew that this was going to be his life's work for God. He gathered a group of Christian friends together and they met regularly at his house in London to make their plans. One of the group travelled all over Britain to gather evidence about the slave trade from sailors and former slaves. He went on board slave ships and measured the holds where the slaves were chained, to show just how small a space each man had. He brought back chains and fetters, handcuffs and thumbscrews. The friends used every way they could think of to make people realise the evils of slavery.

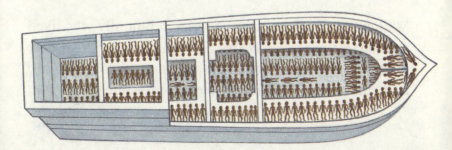

They even had pictures and slogans painted on the bottoms of soup plates. Then, as guests sipped their soup, they were forced to read, "Do away with slavery!", or they would see a picture of a negro and the words "Am I not a Man and a Brother?"

Many people were horrified by the stories of slavery in Britain, and in British ships and Colonies. The group of Christian friends won thousands of people to support their fight, but they knew that this alone was not enough. Slavery would never end until there were laws against it. Someone would have to lead the fight in Parliament to get new laws made, and everyone knew who that person should be. His name was William Wilberforce—a Member of Parliament and a brilliant speaker.

* * * * * *

William Wilberforce came from a rich family who lived at Hull in Yorkshire. He went to Cambridge University where he made many friends, for he was clever, witty and charming. When he was twenty-one years old, he became a Member of Parliament. He enjoyed arguing and debating in Parliament, but he also found plenty of time to be a "man about town". He belonged to five clubs, and spent his evenings in drinking and gambling, and going to dances and parties.

Then when he was twenty-five years old, a great change came over William Wilberforce. He gave up his life of pleasure, and he began to read serious books and study the Bible. "I decided to give the rest of my life to the service of God," he wrote. That was how he came to be one of the group of friends who met at Granville Sharp's house. That was how William Wilberforce came to realise that the war against slavery was going to be *his* life's work for God.

*　　*　　*　　*　　*　　*

It was in 1789 that William Wilberforce stood up in Parliament for the first time to propose a new law against slavery. He spoke for three hours, giving the terrible facts which his friends had gathered about the evils of slavery and the slave trade. "I blame no one person," he said. "Every single one of us is guilty of allowing these dreadful evils to happen."

At first the Members of Parliament listened to him quietly. Some were horrified by the things he described, but others opposed him angrily. Some Members of Parliament owned plantations and had become rich through their slaves' hard work. Merchants and traders who made their living from the slave trade also hated William Wilberforce. He had many enemies, and the new law he proposed was quickly thrown out, but he never gave up trying to have it passed.

Some people mocked him. Some even said he had gone mad. "My mother and relatives in Yorkshire were very worried," wrote Wilberforce. "I had to go back home and show them how cheerful and happy I was, working for God. One of them said, 'If that's madness, I wish other people suffered from it!'"

It was his Christian faith and his Christian friends that gave Wilberforce the strength to go on. One of those friends was John Wesley, the great founder of the Methodist movement. The very last letter Wesley wrote was to cheer Wilberforce on. "If God be for you, who can be against you?" wrote Wesley. "He has called you to this great task. Go on, in the name of God!"

* * * * * *

William Wilberforce went on speaking against slavery, year after year. He spoke in towns all over Britain. He spoke in Parliament, where the new law that he wanted was thrown out time after time. For nearly twenty years he went on with his war against slavery. As time went by, more and more people came to agree with him, and

even in Parliament the number of votes for his new law increased year by year.

In the year 1807, he spoke for the last time in Parliament. When the votes were counted, there were 384 supporting his new law, and only sixteen against it. Everyone rose to cheer William Wilberforce on his great victory. His new law ended British trading in slaves for ever.

But the war against slavery was not over yet. Although the new law forbade the buying and selling of slaves in all British lands, it did not help people who were already slaves. Slavery itself had to be ended—and that took another twenty years.

William Wilberforce lived just long enough to hear that the law of 1833 had been passed by Parliament, saying that all slaves in British lands were now free men. Wilberforce heard the wonderful news as he lay dying. His work for God was done, and the war had ended in victory. Slavery was no more.

Three days later, William Wilberforce died in peace, thanking God with his last breath that he had lived to see the triumph of his cause.

The Champion of Children

There was another kind of slavery in those days—the slavery of children. This is the story of child slaves and the Christians who fought to make them free.

★ ★ ★ ★ ★ ★

In the year 1830, a man named Richard Oastler attended a meeting in the city of Leeds against the slavery of black people. Afterwards he wrote a letter to the city newspaper, the *Leeds Mercury*—a letter which became famous. It said:

"No one is happier than I am that the war against slavery is being fought so strongly. I pray that it will soon be won. But there is worse slavery here—in our own land! In the West Indies a black slave works eleven and a half hours a day. But in England, there are thousands of little children who are made to work in the mills for thirteen hours a day. They are boys and girls between seven and thirteen years of age. They are forced to go to work, ragged and tired and hungry. They are kept at work by the strap of the overseer—just as a slave is driven by the whip of the slave-driver. Do not these English slaves, our own children, need to be protected by laws too?"

Another war had begun, against a different kind of slavery. It had to be fought in Parliament, to get new laws made to protect children, and it was led by a Member of Parliament named Michael Sadler. In order to make the terrible facts known in Parliament, he persuaded witnesses to come to answer questions from Members on his committee.

One witness was Samuel Coulson, the father of a poverty-stricken family. This is what he said in his answers:

"In the busy time, for about six weeks, the girls went to work at three o'clock in the morning. They finished at ten o'clock, or nearly half-past ten, at night. During the day they were allowed fifteen minutes for breakfast, and thirty minutes for dinner. But this time was often spent in cleaning the machines. They had no more than four hours sleep. My wife or I got up at two o'clock to dress them.

"The rest of the time they worked shorter hours— from six o'clock in the morning to half-past eight at night. They were so tired that they sometimes fell asleep while they were eating the little food we had to give them. During the day the children were always so tired that the strap was often used to keep them awake.

"One day my eldest daughter caught her finger in the machine. She had to go to the Infirmary that afternoon, so her pay was stopped for a quarter of that day. She was in Leeds Infirmary for five weeks.

"Wages were three shillings a week—but in the busy time, they were three shillings and sevenpence."

Machines had just been invented in England; coal and iron were both needed—iron to make the machines, and coal to run them. New coal mines had been dug; factories and mills had been built. All of these were busy day and night, and needed many workers. Wages were poor, but people from the countryside were near to starvation and flocked into the towns to earn some money.

Women as well as men worked for low wages, but boys and girls were the cheapest labour of all for the owners of mines and factories. Some parents were so poor that they were forced to send their children to work. Even the little money *they* earned was needed

to buy food. Cruel parents, even if they did not need money badly, sometimes sent their children to work out of greed. Children without parents were sent from their orphanages.

Some Members of Parliament said that hard work was good for children, and the trade of the country would suffer if the Government made laws against children working. Some doctors said that the work did no harm to the health of children. It was Christian people, like Richard Oastler and Michael Sadler, who fought for laws to protect children from cruel work. Why did they do it? Richard Oastler gave the reason in his famous letter to the newspaper: "Christians should feel for children, and work for them, because Jesus loved them."

★   ★   ★   ★   ★   ★

A time came when Michael Sadler lost his seat in Parliament. Since he could no longer continue his fight for the children inside Parliament, he went to a Christian friend named Lord Shaftesbury.

He asked him, "Will you lead the fight for new laws to protect the children and the poor?"

When Lord Shaftesbury discussed it with his wife, he told her, "It would be a work for God."

"Then it is your duty to do it." his wife replied.

From that day on, Lord Shaftesbury spent the rest

of his life in the service of poor and orphan children. He was heir to his rich father's lands and wealth, but his father would give him no help. He had no pay, and he had to exist on his small family income. Sometimes he had to borrow money to feed his ten children and to send them to school. He even refused offers of important positions in the Government so that he could work for the poor. His work went on for fifty years.

Lord Shaftesbury began by going round the mills to see for himself just what was happening. He found that most children started work when they were five years old, although some children were even sent to work at three. He described to Parliament the horrors that he found. Finally, in the year 1844, his new laws were passed, making it illegal for children under eight years old to work in the mills. The laws said also that children between eight and thirteen years of age must not work for more than six and a half hours a day; and that women, and young people from fourteen to eighteen years of age, must not work more than twelve hours a day.

*　　*　　*　　*　　*　　*

So children under eight years old were not allowed to work in mills any more—but mills were often built near coal mines, and there was no law against children working in the mines. So poor and needy parents, and parents who were cruel and greedy, sent their children to work in the coal mines instead. Even some of the miners made their wives and children work in the pits.

There were evils in the mines that were worse than those in the mills, as Lord Shaftesbury found. Children of six and seven years of age worked twelve hours a day down there in the darkness. The youngest children were "trappers". They sat all day by the trapdoors which controlled the flow of air, and opened them to let the sledges of coal go through. For long periods of time, often days on end, they never saw any daylight at all. Some children were even carried to the mines in their night-clothes.

One little girl said, "There's no light and I'm frightened all the time. I'm there from four o'clock in the morning till five o'clock at night."

Often there were accidents. Sometimes a young trapper would fall asleep across the rails, and be crushed by the heavy sledges loaded with coal. Women and older children sometimes fell to their deaths as they struggled to carry heavy bags of coal up the steep and dangerous ladders of the mine shaft.

Sledges filled with coal were pulled along by bigger children, using chains. Other children stood all day long in water, working the pumps. Women, as well as boys and girls, crawled on all fours through the dark, narrow passages, with harnesses for pulling the sledges fastened on their bodies. They suffered terribly from the dark and the damp, the strain of heavy work, and the long hours. Worst of all was the awful effect this had on the growing bodies of children.

*   *   *   *   *   *

Lord Shaftesbury persuaded Parliament to set up a committee to investigate these terrible happenings in the mines, and to publish a report of their findings. When the report appeared, it included drawings as well as words. It showed very clearly the horrors in which children were made to work.

Lord Shaftesbury presented the report to the Members of the House of Commons, saying, "It is a mass of sin and cruelty." They were horrified and quickly passed the new law that he wanted, but it had also to go through the House of Lords, and this was not so easy.

Some of the members of the House of Lords owned coal mines and wanted the cheap labour of children to go on. One of them spoke about the young "trappers". "They are usually cheerful and content," he said. "They pass the time carving bits of wood, making models of windmills and wagons." But eventually Lord Shaftesbury won, and the law was passed.

The new law said that no boys under ten years of age were to work in the mines, and women and girls were not allowed to work in the mines at all. Lord Shaftesbury wrote in his diary: "August 8th, 1842. I went to church and received the sacred bread and wine.

I gave thanks to God for the success with which he has blessed my work for his children."

*　　*　　*　　*　　*　　*

Although Lord Shaftesbury had achieved a great deal, he knew there were other children still in danger. They were the boys who were made to climb up inside the big chimneys of those days, when coal fires were the only way of heating people's homes. They had to sweep away the soot, and sometimes put out chimney fires. They were beaten, and even had fires lit beneath them to make them climb the chimneys. Often a boy was apprenticed to a sweep. This was a terrible fate, for he became the slave of his master. In time, many of these children died from a grim disease called "sooty cancer".

Lord Shaftesbury brought the dreadful facts before Parliament, saying, "I know of one boy aged four and a half years who is forced to go up chimneys." His new law against the wicked practice was passed in 1842. But boys still went on being forced to sweep chimneys, and magistrates did not bother to see that the law was kept. Wealthy ladies did not like brushes and rods being used to sweep their chimneys. "It makes more dirt than the old way," they said. They preferred their chimneys swept by hand—by the young boys.

For thirty years Lord Shaftesbury went on fighting. Then in 1875 he got a law passed which really worked.

This law gave the police power to make sure that no boys were forced to climb chimneys.

*　　*　　*　　*　　*　　*

It was not enough, however, to save children from cruel work in the factories, mills, mines and chimneys. They had to be educated too, and for this schools were needed. Christian teachers set up schools for poor and orphan children, and they asked Lord Shaftesbury to lead their work.

Ragged Schools, as they were called, were set up in many towns, and Lord Shaftesbury made sure that even children who lived in the gutter could go to one. "I found one boy who slept in the big iron roller in Regent's Park, London," he said. He was very proud of the schools, so proud that he said, "I would rather be President of the Ragged Schools than rule over an empire."

On one occasion Lord Shaftesbury's watch was stolen, when he was visiting people in the slums. Next day he found a sack outside his front door. Inside it was a boy, tied up, with a note round his neck saying, "He stole your watch. Do what you like with him." Lord Shaftesbury took the boy straight off to one of his Ragged Schools, to be looked after and educated.

Lord Shaftesbury became famous all over the land as the friend of the poor, and the poor loved him in return. The costermongers of London, who sold food from their carts and stalls in the streets, gave him a donkey as a sign that they had made him a member of their union. Even thieves loved him. Once they planned a secret meeting and asked Lord Shaftesbury to talk to them. Over four hundred thieves were there to meet him, and many of them promised him that they would give up stealing.

When Lord Shaftesbury died in 1885, the streets of London were filled with poor people, mourning for the friend they loved. A monument was set up to honour his memory in the heart of London, in Piccadilly. It was a statue of Eros, the Greek god of love, and it still stands today to remind all who see it of the love Lord Shaftesbury showed as the friend of the poor, and the champion of children.

The Festival of Freedom

Here is the story of the Jewish festival of Passover. It comes from early times, when the ancestors of the Jews were called Hebrews.

*　　*　　*　　*　　*　　*

Passover is the greatest festival of the year for Jews. It comes at the time of year which is our springtime. Today, wherever they live, Jews still keep Passover, with all its ancient customs.

The festival celebrates the time when the Jews of old were delivered from slavery in Egypt. It comes down from the time of Moses, three thousand years ago. But Passover may be even older than that, for it is believed to have come from two festivals of even earlier days.

The first of these festivals also came in springtime, when shepherds rejoiced over their newborn lambs. They offered one of the new lambs as a sacrifice to give thanks to God for his goodness, and to seek his blessing for the future. This festival of the shepherds was called Passover.

One of the customs at the shepherds' festival was to dip a bunch of a special plant called hyssop in the blood of a newborn lamb, and to smear the doorposts of the home with it. People in ancient times believed in demons and evil spirits. They believed that the blood smeared around the door would keep evil spirits from entering the house and protect those who lived in the house.

People who worked on the land and grew crops also had a special festival. They grew barley for making bread, and when harvest time came they offered some of the new barley to God. This was to give thanks for their daily bread and to seek God's blessing for the future. The bread was usually made with leaven. This was dough kept from the last bread-making, and it made the bread rise. For their barley festival, however, the people who worked on the land made special wafers from the new barley without any leaven, and eating unleavened bread became a custom at their harvest festival.

*　　*　　*　　*　　*　　*

It was in the time of Moses that these ancient customs were brought together and given a wonderful new meaning.

The Hebrews had gone to Egypt in search of food during a time of famine. They settled there in a place called Goshen, and the Pharaohs who ruled Egypt were friendly to them. The Hebrews lived in peace in Egypt for four hundred years.

At the end of those years, new Pharaohs came who were not friendly to the Hebrews. These Pharaohs were strong rulers who decided to build towns and fortresses in the delta of the River Nile, where the Hebrews were living. Since the Pharaohs needed hundreds of workers for their great building schemes, they made the Hebrews work as slaves. For many years the Hebrews toiled under the hot sun, making bricks, driven on by the whips of Egyptian taskmasters. How they longed for a leader to deliver them from their cruel slavery and to make them free again!

At last a great deliverer came to lead them out of Egypt—it was Moses. Boldly he went to Pharaoh and demanded freedom for his people in the name of their God. But Pharaoh knew nothing of the God of the Hebrews, and his heart was hard. He refused to let his slaves go free.

Then came terrible happenings in the land of Egypt. One plague after another fell upon the Egyptians. The last was the worst of all. A grim disease attacked the Egyptian children, and even the eldest son of Pharaoh died from it.

Goshen, where the Hebrews lived, was in an outlying part of Egypt, and the disease did not affect them. Since they had smeared their doorposts with hyssop dipped in blood, after the ancient custom, they believed the "spirit of death" had "passed over" their homes without harming their children. So now the custom had a wonderful new meaning for them, and so did the name "Passover".

After the last terrible plague, and the death of his own son, Pharaoh gave in to Moses, and told him he could lead his people free. In their haste to escape, the Hebrews had no time to leaven their bread, so they ate unleavened bread. This was never forgotten, and the custom of eating unleavened bread became part of the Jewish Passover Festival. This ancient custom of the barley harvest now had a wonderful new meaning too.

After their escape from Egypt, Moses led the Hebrews to the holy mountain of Sinai. The huge mountain reached up to heaven—vast, lonely and forbidding. When its peak was hidden in thunder clouds, and storms crashed around the mountain heights, the Hebrews trembled with fear as they thought of the God who lived there.

In ancient times, people believed in many Gods. Each God had a "home" where he "lived" and ruled, such as a mountain, a volcano, a waterfall or a rushing river.

The Hebrews believed that the God of Mount Sinai had gone down to Egypt to save them. But each God belonged to a tribe, and the Hebrews knew that the God of Mount Sinai did not belong to them. So they had to make a treaty of friendship with him, because he had adopted them. They would have to promise to be loyal to him and to live as his chosen people. That was why Moses had brought them to Mount Sinai, the dwelling place of their new God.

*   *   *   *   *   *

The Hebrews made their treaty of friendship with God in a *covenant*. This word means making promises to each other. As their leader, Moses had to make the covenant. He went up the mountain alone to be close to God. He wrote the promises of the covenant with God on two tablets of stone. There were five promises on each tablet, and together they are called the Ten Commandments. The first four Commandments told the Hebrews their duty to God, as his chosen people. The other Commandments told the Hebrews their duty to each other.

At the holy mountain of Sinai, the people promised to keep these Ten Commandments. God wanted more than their prayers and sacrifices: he wanted them to live good lives. This was something strange and new. The Gods of other tribes were often evil in their ways, and they did not care about how their people lived. But the God of the Hebrews *did* care. He was just and fair and good. He wanted his people to be like that, too.

*   *   *   *   *   *

Moses gave his people many other laws besides the Ten Commandments, but they were not all his own ideas. He had been brought up in a palace in Egypt, so he would have learnt the laws of Egypt. He would have heard of the laws of other lands, too, and he would have used them in making laws for his own people.

All later Jewish laws were built on the foundation laid by Moses. They were added to his laws, and became the five Books of Law in the Jewish Bible. Jewish people still live today by the sacred Law of Moses, the prophet and spokesman of God.

*   *   *   *   *   *

The Passover Festival lasts for seven days. The first day and the last day are the most sacred. On those days, there is no work, no school, and religious services are held in the synagogue. The festival begins in the home after long preparation—cleaning the house, making new clothes, and getting special foods ready.

On the first evening, the Passover meal is held at home. Candles are lit and the whole family, with their

friends, sit around the table together. At the head of the table there are two plates. On one plate are three cakes made of unleavened bread, a symbol of the food eaten in haste by the Hebrew slaves before leaving Egypt. A small piece of the middle cake is hidden away, and after the meal the children enjoy searching for it. No leavened bread is allowed in the house during the seven days of the festival.

On the other plate there are five things, each of which is a symbol, with its own special meaning. There is a roasted leg of lamb, a symbol of the lamb offered at the spring festival long ago. There is a baked egg, a symbol of the renewal of life in spring. There are bitter herbs, like horse-radish, symbols of the bitter life of the slaves in Egypt. There are green herbs, symbols of the harvest festival of spring. And there is a brown paste made with nuts, raisins, apple, cinnamon

and wine, which is a symbol of the mortar which the slaves used in their building work for the Pharaoh.

On the table there is a bowl of salt water—a symbol of the tears shed by the slaves during their suffering in Egypt.

During the meal four cups of wine are drunk, standing for the four promises which God made to Moses: "I will bring you out; I will rid you of your slavery; I will deliver you; I will take you to me as my people."

During the meal the youngest child in the family asks his father four questions about the meaning of the Passover Festival. Then his father tells the age-old story of how God delivered his people from their slavery in Egypt. In this way every Jewish child learns the meaning of Passover, and of the symbols that are used in this great Festival of Freedom.

Symbols:
The Star of David

The Star of David is used by Jews all over the world as their symbol. It is used to decorate their synagogues, both inside and outside. It can also be seen on the outside of Jewish shops and on boxes of fruit from the land of Israel.

This Star was used by other peoples, as well as Jews. In ancient times it was used as a decoration, for example in Roman mosaic pavements. It has been found in the remains of an early Jewish synagogue at Capernaum, in the land of Israel. But it was not until much later that it became the Star of David, the great symbol of the Jews.

There are many explanations of this symbol and of how it became the Star of David. One is that the Star is made of two equal triangles. In the Hebrew language of the Jews, and in the Greek language, the letter D is shaped like a triangle. So the Star is made of D and D. These are the first and last letters of the name David, the great King of the Jews long ago. That is how this Jewish symbol may have got its name—Star of David.

There have been times when Jews were made to wear the Star of David as a symbol of shame and disgrace. When Hitler and his Nazis ruled over Germany, they made Jews wear the shape of the Star, cut out of yellow cloth, as a "badge of shame". Jews suffered great cruelty under Hitler. But they could never think of this symbol as shameful. To them the Star of David is a symbol of honour and pride in their people.

Maundy Thursday

In 1983 the festival called Maundy Thursday was on the 31st of March. On that day, Queen Elizabeth II went to the city of Exeter in Devon for a special festival in its ancient cathedral. At the service the Queen presented special purses, with special money inside them, to fifty-seven elderly men and women.

Why did the Queen present these gifts? Why were they presented to exactly that number of elderly men and women? Why is this festival held each year, and what does Maundy Thursday mean?

To answer these questions, we must go back nearly two thousand years.

Each year, on Good Friday, Christians remember how Jesus died on the cross.

On the evening before he was crucified, Jesus held the Last Supper with his twelve disciples. During the meal he shared bread and wine among them, explaining as he did so that these were symbols of his body and blood.

When the supper was over, Jesus acted another symbol. He took a bowl of water and a towel, washed the feet of his disciples and dried them. This was always done by a servant of the house. When Jesus had finished, he said to his disciples, "I have given you an example to show you that you should serve others as I have served you. And I give you a new commandment —love one another, as I have loved you."

The word for "commandment" in the Latin language is *mandatum*, so that in the Latin Bible, Jesus said, "I have given you a new *mandatum*." From this word *mandatum* came our word "maundy". So the Thursday before Good Friday came to be called Maundy Thursday.

On Maundy Thursday it became the custom to wash the feet of others as a symbol of Christian love for them. The custom was kept in churches and monasteries. It became the special custom of kings and queens. However great they were, on this day they followed the example of Jesus and showed their Christian love by kneeling down to wash the feet of the poor.

On Maundy Thursday in the year 1120, Queen Maud, the wife of King Henry I of England, walked with bare feet to Westminster Abbey in London. There she kept the festival by washing the feet of thirteen poor people and giving them money. We know that this custom was kept by later kings and queens of England as well.

About the year 1400, King Henry IV began a new custom at the festival of feet-washing on Maundy Thursday. The number of poor men and women whose feet were to be washed at the festival was to be the same as the years of his age. That was why, in 1572, Queen Elizabeth I at the age of thirty-nine washed the feet of thirty-nine men and thirty-nine women at her Palace of Greenwich on Maundy Thursday.

In 1665, a terrible disease called the Great Plague swept through London. The disease was so infectious that it quickly passed from person to person. This made it dangerous for the monarch to keep the custom of washing feet on Maundy Thursday. Instead, food and clothes were given to the poor people at the festival, as well as money. Good food and good clothes were precious to the poor in those times.

In later years, it was decided to give money instead of food and clothes. King Charles II began the custom of having special silver coins made at the Royal Mint for the presents he gave to the poor on Maundy Thursday. These special coins came to be called Maundy Money.

This custom of giving Maundy Money has continued ever since. Today the rare and valuable silver coins, in fine purses, are presented by the Queen to elderly people on Maundy Thursday. In 1983, fifty-seven were given, because that was the age of the Queen.

Through the centuries, this ancient festival was held at Westminster Abbey in London. Queen Elizabeth II has begun the custom of keeping the festival at cathedrals outside London, so that more people can share in it. That was why, in 1983, the festival of Maundy Thursday was held at the cathedral in Exeter.

Wherever the festival is held, the Queen is always attended by Yeomen of the Guard in their fine red dress, which was the uniform of Tudor times. One of the Yeomen carries the purses on a great silver dish, which he rests on his flat Tudor hat. With the Queen, too, is the Lord High Almoner of her royal court, and his assistants. They carry towels, just as Jesus did at the Last Supper nearly two thousand years ago.

Symbols: The Cross

The cross is a very ancient symbol. The simple cross with four equal arms was used by cave men twelve thousand years ago. From the earliest times it was a symbol of the sun.

The ancient Egyptians wore a cross round their necks, shaped like a T with a loop on top, called the *ankh*. It was a symbol of life. It was buried with the dead, for it looked like a key to open the gate to life after death.

The Indians of America used the cross as a symbol of the gods of rain.

The cross became the great symbol of Christians because Jesus Christ was crucified on a cross. It had to be used secretly until Constantine became emperor of Rome. Before the victory which made him emperor,

he had seen a vision of a great cross of light in the sky, with the words, "Conquer by this sign". So Constantine too became a Christian. From then onwards Christians everywhere were allowed to worship Jesus openly, and to use their symbol of the cross freely.

There are different shapes of cross. There is the T shape, called the cross of St Anthony, who was the first Christian monk; the Greek cross, with arms all of the same length; the X shape, called the cross of St Andrew, who died on a cross of this shape; the Latin cross, with the cross-piece near the top; and the Celtic cross, like the Latin cross with a circle round the head. A cross with a figure of Jesus on it is called a crucifix.

The cross is used everywhere by Christians. Many wear a cross as a necklace, and many make the sign of the cross with their hands. They are using the cross as a symbol—to show their faith, to bring protection against evil, and to seek the blessing of God.

The Light of Life

All light comes from the sun. Without sunlight the moon would be quite dark, for it simply reflects the sun and has no light of its own. Without sunlight, our earth would be like that too—dark, cold and dead.

All life comes from the sun. Without sunlight, plants could not live and grow. The leaves of plants are wonderful food factories. Before a factory can go into production, it needs two things: raw materials, like wood and iron; and energy, like electricity. A leaf uses air, earth and water as its raw materials, and its energy is the light from the sun. That is why these plant factories cannot work at night.

Sunlight gives plants the energy they need to make food for themselves, and in their turn, plants provide food for animals and men. So we depend on sunlight for everything, and we could not live without it.

*   *   *   *   *   *

In early times, men and women worshipped the sun as the greatest God of all, because they knew that they depended on the sun for everything. All over the world there were temples where people sang praises to the great Sun God, and prayed for his future blessings.

In a hot land like Egypt, the Sun God reigned

supreme in the heavens. But at night he sank low in the sky and went into the world of darkness. What mattered to the Egyptians was that the Sun God should triumph over the powers of darkness and night, and rise again at dawn in all his glory.

In cold lands of the north, the Sun God was hardly even seen during the long months of winter. So to the people in those cold lands, what mattered was the return of the Sun God in the spring, to bring new life to the earth.

In lands like Britain, neither very hot nor very cold, the Sun God grew weak and pale in the autumn. Men and women worshipped him with festivals of fire to help him to keep up his strength. For them too it was important that the Sun God should regain his power and glory and bring the new life of spring after the death of winter. The Sun God also gave people the seasons of the year—spring for sowing, summer for ripening and autumn for harvesting. He brought the fruits of the earth for all living things.

      ★   ★   ★   ★   ★   ★

In time, men and women came to believe in a God who had created all things—sun and moon and stars, heaven and earth, plants, trees, animals and people. No longer did they worship the sun as a god, for the sun itself was part of the universe which God had made.

He had given light and life to men as part of his creation.

So light became a symbol instead, standing for truth and for knowledge, for understanding and wisdom. Darkness stood for the opposite—for ignorance and foolishness.

In India, long ago, a prince named Gautama longed to know the truth, and to understand the meaning of life. For a long time he searched for this truth. At last, it came to him, and he "saw the light". He found the truth about life. Now he could teach that truth to others. His disciples called him Buddha, which means "The Wise One", or "The One who found the Light", and they came to be known as Buddhists. Today millions of Buddhists live by the "light" which Buddha brought to men and women.

Christians follow the teachings of Jesus, for in him they see God. They live by the "light" which Jesus brought. One of the sayings of Jesus was, "I am the Light of the World". Christians believe in the truth he taught.

Candles, torches, lanterns and lamps became symbols too, and people used them in their religions to stand for something important. That is why there are religious festivals all over the world in which lights are used as symbols. They are Festivals of Light.

*   *   *   *   *   *

The people of China welcome the coming of spring and the return of light with their Lantern Festival. Their year is divided into "moons" which are like our months. The Lantern Festival comes in the middle of the First Moon.

The Chinese make their famous lanterns in bright colours and in different shapes and sizes for the festival. The lanterns are made with paper, silk, glass and stalks

of wheat, and they are painted and decorated with pictures of famous stories and legends. Children carry their lanterns, hung on tall poles, in happy processions.

The Chinese dragon is a very old and popular symbol of good fortune, bringing happiness and good luck. At the Lantern Festival, a huge dragon is carried in procession through the streets. It is made of bamboo and it is brightly coloured with paper or silk. Gifts for the dragon of good fortune are hung from the top windows of houses, and the men carrying the dragon stand on each other's shoulders to reach up and seize the presents.

The Lantern Festival is also celebrated in the home. There are special foods and fine feasts for the family. Presents are given between family and friends, and everyone enjoys the Festival of Lanterns.

*   *   *   *   *   *

People of Japan who follow the Shinto religion pay great honour and respect to their ancestors. They remember them at the Festival of Lanterns which in Japan is in the month of July. Japanese people believe that this is the time when the spirits of their ancestors come back to earth and visit their former homes. So for each family this festival is a special time to pay honour to their ancestors.

The whole family gathers at home for the festival

and when evening falls, they visit the tombs of their ancestors. There they burn incense and hang up their lanterns. They believe that the light of the lanterns will guide the spirits of their ancestors and welcome them to the family home. Children of the family are told stories about the goodness of their ancestors and about their fine deeds. This is to encourage the children to want to be like them.

The three days of the festival in the home end with a meal in honour of the family's ancestors. It is held in the best room in the house. Small pieces of favourite foods are placed on the table, so that the spirits of the family's ancestors can take the food back with them on their return journey to the world of spirits.

★   ★   ★   ★   ★   ★

In India, the New Year of the Hindu religion begins with a festival called Diwali, which means Festival of Lights. It is partly in honour of Lakshmi, the Goddess of fortune and prosperity, so this festival is specially important to traders and businessmen. They open new account books for the coming year to record their buying and selling. At the festival they pray that the Goddess will bring them good fortune and help them to prosper in their trading. Hindus believe that during the festival of Diwali, the Goddess will visit homes that are well prepared and well lit up, and bring good fortune to the family. So every home is carefully cleaned and decorated, and everything is dusted and polished. Most important of all, the home is lit up with many oil lamps.

On the second day of the festival, the family stays at home. Hindu people believe that it is a time when evil witches and bad spirits are at large, and they recite spells to drive them away. The following morning, everyone gets up early. They light even more lamps and welcome their friends, while the children enjoy themselves, letting off crackers.

Sikhs of India celebrate the festival of Diwali too. Sikhs live by the teachings of their ten Gurus or Teachers. Their sixth Guru, a warrior hero, is specially remembered at the festival. Every temple, and especially the famous Golden Temple of Sikhs at their holy city of Amritsar, is lit up for the Festival of Lights.

*   *   *   *   *   *

Jews have their Festival of Lights as well. It is called Hanukkah, which means Dedication. It celebrates the time in 165 B.C. when the Jews won back their holy Temple at Jerusalem from their pagan rulers. The pagan idols were thrown out, and the Temple was dedicated afresh to the worship of God in a joyful festival. The sacred gold candlestick, shaped like a tree with its seven branches, was alight all through the eight days of the festival.

Today Jews still keep Hanukkah in their homes and in their synagogues. In the home there is a special candlestick for this festival, which usually has eight branches for candles. Sometimes it has a ninth branch, called "the servant", which is used to light all the others. The servant candle is used to light one candle on each night of the festival, so that on the last night of the festival all eight candles are alight together. This light from the candles which increases night by night is like faith in God which from a small beginning grows stronger and stronger.

Children enjoy Hanukkah too. They have parties and presents, and they hear once more the story of the first Festival of Lights.

Christians have their Festival of Lights at Christmas. Christmas trees are decorated with lights, and carols are sung by candle-light, to honour the birth of the child whom Christians believe to be the "Light of the World".

Christians use lights at their great festival of Easter as well. In some lands it begins at midnight. It is like that in Greece, where Easter is the greatest festival of the year. The church is in darkness as the people gather, until, at midnight, the priest lights a single candle. Then, one by one, the people light their candles from his candle. The light grows more and more, until every candle is lit and the church is filled with light. Then the joyful cry rings out—"Christ is risen!"

Symbols: Yang and Yin

This symbol is seen everywhere in the land of China.
It is used to decorate gates
and houses and things in the
house. It is a circle made of two parts. They are
opposites, but, together, they make one circle. They
belong together and balance each other.

This symbol comes from the religion of China called
Tao, which means The Way. Tao is the way people
should follow to become wise. Tao shows people how
to live. It is the Way of Yang and Yin.

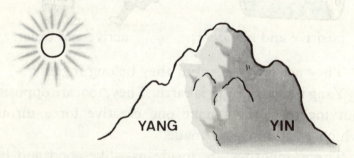

A hill has two sides. One side is in the sun, so it is
light. The other side is in the shade, so it is dark. The
sunny side is called Yang. The dark side is called Yin.
So Yang and Yin are opposite sides of the same hill.
They belong together.

Yang is summer, Yin is winter. They are opposites, but they belong together.

Everything is like that—

light and darkness;

day and night;

white and black;

male and female;

positive and negative;

active and quiet.

They are opposites, but they belong together.

Yang is heaven, Yin is earth. They, too, are opposites, but together, they make one creative force through which everything was made.

These opposites are inside us—like good and bad, kindness and cruelty, love and hate. These opposites are in all of us, whether we like it or not. We must learn how to live with them, and keep them in balance, if we want to be happy. That is the way of wisdom. That is the Way of Tao.